Every _____

as to

What to Expect When She's Expecting

Read this from cover to cover.

Best Regards.

W. Grant Eppler

By
William Grant Eppler

Furlip Publishing
SACRAMENTO

Every Guy's Guide

as to

What to Expect When She's Expecting

A Furlip Publishing Company Book
First Edition February 2000
Second Edition April 2001

For Information: Furlip Publishing
900 Fulton Avenue, Suite 100
Sacramento, California 95825
Everyguysguide.com

Library of Congress Control Number 2001089448
IBSN 0-9656701-1-2

Edited by Ruth Davis Barr
Illustrations by Iam
Cover Layout/Book Design by Kunder Design Studio

10 9 8 7 6 5 4

Printed in the United States of America
US $11.95

Special thanks to:

Jay Michael, Jr., for inspiring the writing of this book,

Dr. Melanie Marchant, for insisting that I write this book,

Ruth Davis Barr, who literally had red pens explode in her hands spraying ink over two sweats outfits and her new couch while editing and re-editing (I owe her two sweats outfits and a new couch),

Pamela Garibaldi, the English teacher who taught me how to write, and re-write, and re-write, and re-write, and re-write and. . . ,

Dr. Perkins, whose great mind helped develop these Guy-ish thoughts,

Kunder Design Studio, for being able to read my mind when I couldn't and for creating exactly what I envisioned,

My entire family,

and most importantly,

Melinda Michael Eppler, for marrying me, for putting up with me, for having our child, and for giving me more to love in my life than I could have ever imagined.

Every  Guy's Guide

as to

What to Expect When She's Expecting

Epplerlogue

Every **Guy's** Guide

2

Babies and Kids

Chapter 3   Hero for a Knight   page 121

Books published by Furlip Publishing are available at quantity discounts on bulk purchases for premium, educational, fund raising, and special sales use. For details please call (916) 488-5974.

chapter one

Pre-ramble
The Telling

Day 1.

Clad in work boots, jeans, my favorite golf hat with a real, dried, turkey-sized bird dropping in the center of my company's logo, a golf glove (our dog had eaten my leather work gloves), a stained-used-to-be-white golf sweater, a leather tool belt complete with 32oz framing hammer, speed square, tape measure, chalk line, black ink marker, construction pencils, and a few handfuls of two and three inch wood screws, I ambled across the street toward home, with my backside, knees, golf glove, and boots all completely covered with a drying half inch of clay...

It was December 30th. A heavy rain with high winds had come through Northern California before Christmas and created havoc for thousands of Californians. Many people went without power for weeks, many were flooded, and our new neighbors, Jason and Jenny, had lost a fence. New in the neighborhood and having some time on my hands, I offered to help them re-build it.

Building the fence was a difficult task, as the old fence presided over two slopes and the property edge fell away sharply. Rainy weather combined with the clay that Jason dug up from the postholes and fecklessly dispersed on the downhill slope, created very slick conditions. On more than one occasion we ended up with a muddy backside, clayed knee, mock clay hand cast, or a combination of all three.

Jason and I had the fence posts up and level. We had attached the cross supports for the fence slats. The hard work was finished and the fun work was about to begin. We were going to use our new cordless power drills. Jason had received his for Christmas, and I, immediately upon seeing his and developing a severe case of power drill envy, had raced out and purchased one also.

NOTICE TO ALL WOMEN: If your husband has been dreaming of cordless power drills all year, and you have prior knowledge that his neighbor and new friend is getting one for Christmas, you can actually save money by breaking down and buying your husband what *he wants* and giving it to him at Christmas.

Jason and I were formulating how we were going to proceed when my wife called and spoke to Jenny. Jenny relayed the message through Jason, "Grant, could you come home when there is a break in the action? Nothing is wrong, just come home for a minute," she had requested. After relaying the message, Jason gave me the questioning guy-eye, to which I replied with a laugh and a shrug, "I wish... but she doesn't have a thing for construction workers."

A guy could always hope.

So there I was, rhythmic sounds and movement from the dangling tool belt, melodically plodding home leaving muddy footprints and droplets of clay along the way. Talking aloud to myself, I said, "Couldn't this wait, damn-it! I can't go inside... I'm covered in mud... look, I'm leaving footprints on the street," and to a car driving by slowly, its occupants chuckling and pointing, "Hey, what are you looking at?"

I arrived at my front door and found it locked. This did nothing to lessen my frustration toward the unwarranted constuctus interruptus. I was thinking, "What is it with this weird-ass message she left. This is very unlike Melinda," as I rang the doorbell and waited.

Melinda answered the door with a dreamy, faraway smile. I, of course, immediately started in with the diatribe I had rehearsed since I'd received her message. "Honey, I can't come in, I am covered in mud, I'd have to completely undress. We need to finish the fence before dark. What's wrong?" She continued beaming at me with her wacky smile. She wasn't smiling at the outfit... she'd seen it before; she was looking right through me, and I considered that perhaps she'd done some early drinking.

"I just thought you would like to know you are going to be a father," she said with a balmy smile, waiting for the meaning of her words to work their way through my forty-two-foot thick concrete skull.

Delirium set in.

I vaguely remember hugging her and kissing her and feeling overjoyed. I remember her saying that was all she wanted to tell me. I remember saying that Jason and I were going to need cigars and Melinda volunteering to go purchase some for us.

What I actually remember, what I could attest to in a court of law as the actual truth, is what Jason said to me when I found my way back to their patio and the former focal point of my existence; the fence.

"Dude, are you okay? You looked shocked! Is something wrong?" Jason asked with a tone of concern. "No, nothing's wrong, everything is right, I am going to be a father!"

It didn't take nearly as long for these words to register with Jason; I am sure that different materials were used for his cranial construction. We shook hands and high-fived. He then said, "Go be with your wife, man, we can finish this later." To which I replied, "No, no. We are going to finish this fence today."

And we did. Melinda showed up with Macanudos for all. Jason and I, eventually dizzy from smoking the cigars while working, finished the fence in time for his post-Christmas family gathering.

Every time I drive by that fence I think to myself, "that is a good, straight, and strong fence. We built that fence on the day Melinda told me I was going to be a father."

The point to all this is that you can expect the conditions of *the telling* to be less than perfect, less than romantic, and less dramatic than it is in the movies and commercials. Even though you may be out of work, back in school with your wife supporting you, and you are dressed as I was, there is definitely something magical that happens deep in the heart of a guy who hears the words, "You are going to be a father."

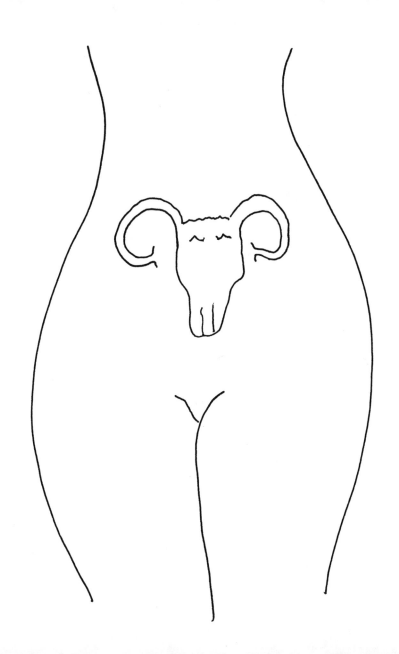

chapter two

The Talk

Day 14.

Guys receive very little information regarding anything that is really important in life, that is, of course, except for the weather. And almost all discussions about the weather are about the weather that has already happened; i.e. the past. Guys are generally left to fend for themselves when it comes to dealing with women.

Most guys can recall the seventh or eighth grade sex education films we had to watch that told of, and showed us pictures of, the super-secret "Phillip Eno tubes" that each woman has within her body. We remember these films for several different reasons: It was so mysterious, so secret, that we had to get signed notes from our parents (most were forged) reading, "It is OK for Johnny to see a 'uteran.'" We were then separated from the girls and ushered into a big dark gym. All of the male teachers from math, English, phys. ed., and even the principal were in attendance and they clearly looked uncomfortable. We were scared mostly because *they* looked so scared. The net retained information from these all-important classes was:

1. There appeared to be a ram's head inside each woman's body.
2. Soon the girls were going to have to attend an extra period at school.
3. Most girls worked for the government (and carried around inside their stomachs the super secret aforementioned tubes

implanted in the antlers of the ram's head).

4. The class dork, Johnny "Cletus" Miller, asking with all seriousness, the ever-important question by re-quoting exactly what we were told, "If it is the male that determines what the baby is going to be, can he decide to have a baby horse, or maybe a golden retriever instead?" Hey! It made sense to us at the time.

5. And most importantly, there would be times when girls would not want to do fun things like go swimming, etc ... because of the homework from the extra class the girls had to take.

The few moments listed above, combined with the two-minute "birds and the bees" discussion we had with our fathers after going to the zoo, is about all that guys get in the way of intelligent discussion regarding sex and the opposite sex. That is, except for the ever present "If you hurt my daughter, I'll get my shotgun," father-in-law-to-be to son-in-law-to-be discussion held conveniently on the day you ask for his daughter's hand in marriage.

Intelligent male-to-male discussions regarding women are so rare that even male comedians routinely poke fun at our lack of knowledge regarding the opposite sex. I heard a comedian say, "Guys are on their own when it comes to dealing with women. You women have Planned Parenthood; you can get pamphlets, flyers, and books on your bodies and your sexuality. Women get tampon commercials, women get Gyne-Lotrimin commercials: guys get none of these, guys are on their own, all guys get is **DICK!**" which he emphasized by yelling the last word and grabbing his crotch, in that primal masculine way. To a great extent, this is true.

Perhaps the most important male/male discussion I have had regarding women, and in particular pregnant women, was with my brother-in-law, Jay. He asked me to lunch to discuss and describe examples of what a father-to-be could expect during the coming months of gestation. He actually said, not in the same way that the comedian had said, that women have all the books, pamphlets and flyers needed to help guide them through these months. He found that guys have very little, if anything, to reference from a man's point of view to help them through these wonderfully difficult months. Having just gone through it, (producing a son) he wanted to share his first-hand observations and learned behavioral patterns, in the hopes of sparing his sister and me some of the growing pains he and his wife had experienced.

We had a great lunch. He shared funny stories of some of his pregnant wife's peculiar behavioral situations to help illustrate his various points. Now, seeing that I have been known to hyperbolize or embellish the truth to help lubricate an otherwise dry topic or story, I have chosen not to reproduce in writing the instances that he gave to drive home the most important piece of information that I have gleaned so far. Do not, however, allow this to deter you from fully understanding this most significant condensed piece of information:

Do not argue with a pregnant woman.

Do not argue with a pregnant woman. What she experiences the baby experiences. Her discomfort, physical and/or mental, is the baby's discomfort. Lest we forget our goal: The goal here is to deliver a healthy, happy baby a few months from now. All that lends itself to this goal should be incorporated, because a happy baby is one of life's biggest joys.

Do not argue with a pregnant woman for it serves no purpose.

With all of the extra hormones that have been activated, you may find there is little emotional stability. There may be no sane point of reference from which to advocate your beliefs. Whatever semblance of sanity this woman previously held that you had loved and admired, can vacate her mind, soul and body in a millisecond (kind of like the days before the wedding). What used to be OK can now be not OK in a nanosecond. The reasons for which she fell in love with you can now make her feel sick to her stomach. And worst of all, she may not hesitate to tell you about it!

Do not argue with a pregnant woman. It is best to claim responsibility for all problems big and small before they become an issue between you. A simple real-life example: My pregnant wife and I went to the movies, in a not-so-good part of town. She drove. She left the headlights on (to light up the parking lot? To make it easier to find the car in broad daylight?). When we came out, the battery was dead. Having remembered the discussion with my brother-in-law and this new pregnancy credo, instead of making some snarky remark I immediately chimed with, "I'm sorry honey, it's my fault. I saw you turn them on, I made a mental note to check them before we went into the movies, I forgot to do so, It's my fault." You will be amazed at how liberating it can be to *not* fight.

I am not inferring that a pregnant woman cannot make and hold a cogent, intelligent, and valid argument! I am simply saying that if you can help to avoid pointless arguments and she can remain steadily happy, it will help the baby.

Hopefully, at some point a month or so after delivery, she will remember the gallant swallowing of pride and bile you went through to avoid fighting with her during those trying months. If not, you still avoided arguments for six months!

Do not argue with a pregnant woman. . .*UNLESS*. . .she is smoking, drinking, or you have some other huge investment at stake. Protecting one's family, home, and possessions still falls on the guy's shoulders in most relationships. Not wanting your pregnant wife to drink or smoke falls under protecting the health of your child and your family. The validity of this argument is documented with so much medical evidence that there is no counter argument. If your wife was a smoker before pregnancy and gave it up cold turkey, she may try to sneak a puff or two a couple of weeks after quitting. Hopefully, this regression will make her turn green and feel so sick that you can support her in sickness and in not smoking, rather than fighting with her.

If that fails, you must make your feelings known, strongly, evenly, and unequivocally.

chapter three

Keeping the Appointment
Attending My First Obstetrical Exam

Please Note: I was nervous writing this chapter, I am nervous re-reading this chapter. Perhaps this is normal. If you have no intention of being this involved in your wife's gestation, or if your wife likens taking you to her doctor with moving to Chernobyl next week, SKIP THIS CHAPTER!

Day 22.

I am sitting in the sterile office of my wife's obstetrician, a place where few men venture, judging from the beady-eyed looks I am getting from the women in the waiting room. My wife has not yet arrived. I am sure that they think of me as some sort of perverted cat burglar, and that this office is some kind of sacred place where female secrets are kept in vaults. Little do they know that no guy truly wants to know these secrets!

It is just one of those things, guys. You've got to do it. While attending the first pregnancy-related OB visits with your wife does not sound like an earth-shattering, backbreaking show of support, you should at least offer to go. And when your wife says that she doesn't want you to go, it is wise to insist that you want to (what are you, nuts?). This simple two hour commitment (appointment + lunch) blurs and transcends the distinct barriers that separate men and women. I know what you are thinking, "Who wants to cross those lines? Those lines help dictate societal order. I am comfortable being a caveman sort of guy!" and while you may feel as uncomfortable as I did, she will never forget that you were there.

Where is women's lib when a guy needs a magazine to read at the obstetrician? There are no "normal" magazines to read. Where are all of the *Sports Illustrated* magazines? All I can find is *Woman*, *People*, and *Parent*. Ah, safe! A *Car and Driver.* I thought it was all over with!

My wife has just arrived and she doesn't seem overjoyed to see me. At least I am no longer alone in the girl's club. I guess if the roles were reversed, and some doctor were about to ask me to "relax, and scoot down," while my naked legs were spread, I might briefly lose my social acumen.

She has perfect timing, for the receptionist just called our name. It is time. Now is the time to come clean. This is where the rubber hits the road, and the men are separated from the boys (I wish I were a boy again).

What is a good ol' boy from Oklahoma doing here?

Male self-introspection at the obstetrician. Who would'a thunk?

Honestly, I was a nervous wreck. You may be too.

Whew! I made it. It wasn't that bad! And do I have a lot to share with you! First off, they ask what seemed to be two zillion questions. Then you are both informed of the three trillion tests that she is going to have to endure in the next six weeks. Now is the time to speak up and do your male duty by asking any and all stupid guy questions that you can think of, and to inform the doctor of any and all sexually transmitted diseases (STD's) that you have ever had. Not only will this alleviate any of your fatherly fears and give you and your wife something to fight about on the way to lunch, it will also give the doctor and your wife something to laugh about next time they see each other. "Can you believe he actually said 'dick warts'? Did you see the look on his face?" they will say, laughing that timeless women-laughing-at-men laugh.

And now, to keep you up to date and prepared for what you are about to encounter, I am going to briefly and graphically describe what transpires at the first pregnancy OB exam. I don't necessarily want to relive this, but if someone had told me what to expect, I would not have been so nervous. After the three zillion questions, you are ushered into a room where your wife immediately tears off all of her clothes except for her bra, and leaps nimbly up onto the table (I know, we all wish we had a room like this at home). She then covers herself with a paper blanket. It is recommended that you make small talk now. "How 'bout them Packers?" is what I said. It didn't seem appropriate at the time (she is a 49er fan), but then again, nothing would have. The doctor enters and continues her conversation with you interspersed with commands such as, "Relax, and scoot down, give me your heels." Then the doctor extends this groovy 6000 watt gyno light from the wall (I wish't we'd had one'a them'n our day). This light lights up the entire southern region. It is also a heat lamp, I was informed later.

Armed with a modicum of social etiquette, I quickly moved to the non-business end of the small room.

The doctor then dons examination gloves, lubricates one, and proffers up with this steel, seven-inch convex and concave-duckbill-shaped ratcheted apparatus. Casually the doctor says, "This is going to be a little uncomfortable, you are going to feel a little pressure here."

Yikes.

It was uncomfortable and I did feel the pressure until the doctor asked, "How 'bout them Rams?"

Thoughts raced through my mind, "It must have been the doc's *Car and Driver* magazine, and that must be her cool Acura Legend with big fat tires in the parking lot" and "Any guy that is not at least fifty-one percent scared shitless pondering childbirth and fatherhood, is absolutely, certifiably crazy."

It was all worth it though, as during our lunch, my wife looked at me with loving eyes and said to me, "Thank you for coming with me today."

She genuinely meant it.

Since this auspicious occasion, I have spoken to many fathers who did not participate in this aspect of the pregnancy, and many more guys who vowed not to when the time came. One friend stated that he did not even want to be in the delivery room during the birth of his child. All of these feelings are natural, and as each couple is different, there is no right or wrong.

Well... Actually... There is. Your wife is right with whatever she decides is the best approach and, if you disagree with her (you guessed it!) you are wrong.

Maybe so... but does she have one of these?

.

chapter four

Male Nesting
Eliminating Risk

Day 35.

As it was when we were young, having the chores done before going out to play is always beneficial. After asking other expectant fathers, I found the urge to nest occurs sooner in some males than in their pregnant female counterparts.

Guys who have their work done, their chores done, and their cars clean tend to feel more liberated. Who wouldn't?

Hearing that you will now have to re-arrange the furniture, condense the home office or guest room, finish the bathroom or deck project that has been ongoing for several years, and baby-proof the household tends to add stress to the life of the average guy who cares about such things and wants the best for his soon-to-be family. I recommend that you start getting your house in order as soon as possible.

It is a **flat ton** of work. The sooner you start, the more you accomplish, little by little, the less that will need to be done when the crunch-time comes. I am not talking about anything to do with the actual baby room. You will probably have little say in that area anyway (see chapter seven). And remember, it is prudent to wait regarding the baby's room until the seventh month or so in case something unexpected were to happen.

I am talking about finishing off the running list of outside chores like cleaning out the gutters, trimming trees, building fences, and completing the construction projects. Unless you are wealthy, money may become too tight to afford these projects later on, and it is better to finish them early in the term to minimize any potential risk or injury to you or your mate. You don't want to fall off a ladder and hurt your back, only to have your eight months pregnant wife help you to the hospital. The stress alone should be avoided. Likewise, it is important to remove or repair any semi-dangerous situation, such as a loose handrail on the back stairs, or an uneven brick or tile on the patio. At some point, no matter how safe you make the home, your wife will probably trip and take a header. The idea here is to minimize any and all potential risk of your wife injuring herself or the child due to something that could have been avoided.

Some simple questions you may want to ask yourself: Do you have smoke detectors? Fire extinguishers? Do they all work? Replace all batteries in the smoke detectors and have all of the fire extinguishers refilled. If renting, your landlord may pay for most of the above basic upkeep. Make a list of all the items that may need repair. Mail your landlord a nice note explaining that you are expecting a baby and that you are trying to help minimize any potential risk by providing a list of items that need to be repaired.

You may also want to ask your landlord about the paint your rental currently shows. Is it lead free?

The reason that this can be important is that a friend's baby learned to crawl to the front window, scratch off the paint with his fingernails, and eat it, before he learned to walk! Evidently, it tastes sweet (I've always wondered about him, and his dad). There are new lead tester kits on the market, making it easy to identify the lead content in any painted surface.

Now is a good time to do any and all repair work to all of your vehicles, such as brakes, tune-ups, tires and the like, before the money runs out. Just wait until you see how much a little person's dresser costs. You would think that since one-fourth of the materials were used, they would be less expensive: you would be wrong. These outside projects and chores and auto repairs should be done, if possible, in the first trimester.

In the second trimester, you will have plenty of time to work on the inside projects; however, if painting or wallpapering, be sure to check that all paints and glues are lead free and pregnancy safe. Always provide adequate airflow (open all windows and doors) and drying time. If these chores can be done while your wife is away, all the better.

It is a good time to clean out all of the closets and the garage, attic (extra careful on that ladder, Daddy-O), and basement. Have a yard sale (extra $) or make a charitable donation (tax write-off), to clear your house or apartment of the unwanted, unused stuff that seems to crawl into your closets when you are not looking. Not only can you earn a little extra cash, you can make more room for all of the accouterments that a baby necessitates. Unless you live in a 5,000 square foot home, you will need the extra closet and storage space.

NOTE: If you do have a yard sale, or a financial plan, set aside some money for a two or three day vacation during the first six months of pregnancy. While time off will be at a premium when the baby comes, a brief respite for your wife from the everyday grind, and a little break for you from all of these damn chores will be sorely needed.

Who knew it was going to be this much work for us guys? If you have accomplished half of the stuff in this chapter, and carrying the child is half of what we've heard that it is for the last quadrillion years, you both will deserve a break from it all. And it is best to plan this getaway while she is still mobile, and well before her delivery date.

The third trimester is home time. No heavy lifting, for either of you. Her pregnancy books will have you carrying everything, everywhere, like a wayward, simpleminded pack mule. Extra care should be employed when undertaking any and all extra strenuous, overtly dangerous events (sporting, hunting, pool room brawls: "Look, papa got no teef").

You can also help to clean all of your kitchen cupboards and kitchen drawers, defrost the refrigerator, and clean out the linen cabinets and dresser drawers. Clean and oil your tools and put them all away. You won't be needing them for six months or so. Change all of the light bulbs, inside and out (careful on that ladder, Pops). Anything that you can do to make your household take on its cleanest and most shipshape form will reap big dividends after the child is born.

I know it seems that I am being some kind of leather-necked drill instructor here. No one can read this to-do list and not feel oppressed. What we are trying to accomplish, what we are trying to prepare for, is ninety days of **NO CHORES** (except cleaning and shopping). **YES!** There *is* a reward!

Remember, you will be going at it full-bore for about three months. You may only get three to six hours of sleep per night, for three or thirty-six months in a row. We all know how dangerous sleep deprivation can be. The last thing you need to be worried about is climbing a ladder with a chainsaw, or your auto breaking down on the side of the road with your pregnant wife (god forbid), or infant child. All of the above advice is intended to try and eliminate risk, and 80% of the above falls squarely upon your shoulders.

Good luck, men. Fall out, and get to it!

KEY WORDS
FROM BOB CLUFF:

"ME"

"US"

"THEM"

chapter five

Universal (male) Voices

Day 47.

During the last month and a half I have heard more guys share their views and wisdom regarding maleness, fatherhood, and husbandry than I have heard in the previous thirty-one years. These views were shared with me at social functions such as New Year's celebrations and children's birthday parties. You won't believe how toasted people can get at a one-year-old's birthday party! I cannot quote each person word for word as I had hoped because I wrote most of the original notes on napkins, which ended up being those little wadded pieces of paper that you find in your jeans after washing.

The best quote that I can attribute to one person, however, came from my sister-in-law's father, Mr. Robert Cluff. Mr. Cluff is a kind, amiable man, and as he and I stood in the kitchen of his daughter's home, he shared these thoughts about life and parenthood. "There are, very simply, three phases of life for men. I call the first phase the *me* phase. Everything that you do in the first phase of your young life usually affects you, and you alone." Smiling, he added with a devilish sparkle in his eyes, "It *was* a pretty good time wasn't it, Grant?" I remember reeling from the blow of the knowledge that I had, in fact, left the first phase of my three-part life behind, and was firmly rooted in the second phase.

I interrupted Mr. Cluff to find a pen, something to write on, and another adult beverage. As I could only find a red pen and a red napkin to write on, I am still laboring to decipher my notes.

"But then you get married, settle down, and nine times out of ten, start a family, thereby entering into phase two, the them phase," he continued, not missing a beat.

"Now you have a wife and perhaps a child on the way, as you do now Grant," he stated, "and every little thing, and any little thing that you do affects and effects *them*. You begin to realize that your options are becoming less abundant, as you worry about *them*. You try to provide for *them*; you must set up a college fund for *them*; everything you do centers around *them*. This period of your life lasts approximately twenty-five years, and will make or break most men," he paused ominously for effect, "but if you make it through that phase, and give it your all, you progress into the *us* phase. I believe this to be the best phase of all. If you have planned it right, you are free from almost all debt. Your children are grown and beginning families of their own, whom you get to see and contribute to as you see fit. Having worked and planned, you can do almost anything you want, within reason. You are happy, as you have led a fulfilled life, and are free from most of the social constraints that a young man must adhere to. It is just you and your spouse, free to do whatever you want to do."

It is kind of sad to admit outright that the first phase of a man's life is slipping away, and that he is entering the second phase as Mr. Cluff sees it. It would appear, however, that Mr. Cluff is correct, given that everything in this book lends itself to the *them* phase, to doing what is best for *them*. It is not that we are getting old, it is that we are growing up.

Thank you, Mr. Cluff.

Additionally: Did you know that a dove mates for life? When a dove's spouse dies, the remaining dove never re-mates. My father-in-law informed me of this when I asked for his daughter's hand in marriage. He has restated this occasionally throughout the years.

Current Surface

LT RAIN/DRIZZLE MOD/HVY RAIN

H

Storm
Warning

chapter six

Keeping the Appointment
Part Deux

Day 48.

We went there again, the place with the mauve walls and rose-colored trim. Again I received scornful looks from my wife's doctor when I stood up during the examination, raised my hands into the air to signal victory, and made those raucous cheering noises heard at a professional football game.

I had just listened to the sounds of a new life forming.

We had heard, through the use of Doppler radar, the sound of our child's heart beating. And yes, it is the same Doppler radar used by the local television station to help them guess at the weather.

It was extremely wild. There was my wife, lying on that table again... with her doctor holding this little microphone unit (a phallic shaped gizmo with a phone-type cord attached to a little hand-held speaker and digital register) to my wife's lower stomach.

"Crash," a loud ominous sound echoed like a thunderstorm in the Midwest. The speaker volume was at its highest level and as it was directed at me, I jumped back and asked with all of the diplomacy I could muster, "What the hell was that?" The doctor answered my question with, "Your child kicked. Here, let me turn this down a little."

My wife smiled.

The doctor repositioned the microphone and the unit emitted a determined repetitive sound, "Duujge, Duujge, Duujge, Duujge, Duujge, Duujge, Duujge, Duujge, Duujge." The doctor said to us, "That is your child's heart beat, 160 beats per minute, that's perfect!"

"Crash," the ominous thunder sounds again echoed throughout the room, and you could almost feel the static electricity of the lightning storm that would follow if you were 1,100 miles to the east.

"Another kick," the doctor explained.

My wife laughed and the Doppler radar unit went noisily crazy, emitting torrents of crackling sounds until the doctor pulled the microphone from her abdomen. "Sorry," my wife said as she grinned from ear to ear. Reflecting on it, I don't think I had ever seen her so simply happy. "OK, I'm ready," she stated, after composing herself. The doctor replaced the microphone, "Duujge, Duujge, Duujge, Duujge, Duujge, Duujge, Duujge, Duujge, Duujge," then the doctor moved the microphone around and the "Duujge, Duujge, Duujge," faded ever softer until a new sound took shape.

"Whoooshz...... Whoooshz......
Whoooshz...... Whoooshz...... Whoooshz...... Whoooshz......
Whoooshz......," came a feather soft, breezy quiet, whispering sound, similar to a slow wind through a willow in the spring. "That is your blood passing through the placenta," the Doctor stated offhandedly, obviously immune to this awe-inspiring sound.

Imagine...

As the doctor again moved the microphone around, the everpresent heart beat of my wife could be heard in the background, like the sound of T-Rex approaching in the movie Jurassic Park, "Baum.................. Baum....................
Baum..................... Baum..................…
Baum....................."

At one point the doctor had all three sounds equidistant to each other, overlaid and over-playing each other, those melodic sounds of life(s) in harmony. I am not sure if there is another sound that carries as much promise and goodwill toward all peoples as the sounds I heard that day.

I wish I could include a recording of it to play for you.
Thank you Mr. Doppler.

Perhaps if you took a cassette recorder to the appointment, you could record those awe-inspiring sounds.

William Grant Eppler

chapter seven

The Selling

Day 65.

My god man, RUN FOR YOUR LIFE.

Collect all of your credit cards and cut them up!

Locate your checkbook and record all outstanding checks.

Secure your 401K accounts, and check on any investments and savings.

You are about to be entangled in the biggest spending event ever!

From the day of her birth, your lovely intelligent, sensible wife was programmed to be a mom. After hearing the heartbeat and seeing the room that you cleared and cleaned for the expected arrival of someone to throw a football with, your wife will take on the posture and determination of that timeless old woman at the K-Mart blue-light special underwear sale table who throws elbows like Charles Barkley under the basket and plows a path through the opposition like Charles Haley to get to and KEEP her sale items.

Go out and buy some Everlast boxer's training headgear men, you are going to need it. If not from the blows that she throws at you, from the agonizing, helpless, beat-your-head-against-the-wall frustration you will feel when your wife comes home (ten weeks pregnant) and says she just put a down payment on an Italian designer crib, because (get this) "the salesman said" they might be out of stock when the time comes! Mind you, I do not advocate that newborns sleep on hardwood floors, but let's remember, he is a salesman! His job is to sell the crib today! And of all the lame excuses to accept from a salesperson for buying something now: he might be *out*?

It is his job to be *in*! That's why they call it *in*ventory!

Why do this so soon? If I had a cozy, warm, safe place to sleep every night for the next six months, I would not be renting an apartment now because there might not be any apartments available six months from now.

Perhaps I was being a tad anal when, five weeks into pregnancy, I tore up and cleaned out the office to make way for the baby's room (Male Nesting, Chapter 3). During this time period, my wife was busily circling $420 worth of baby sheets and bumper pads in catalogues. Circling stuff and planning, I could live with.

Even the fact that they were circled by her caused me undue strain as I am the fiscal agent in our family; however, I now understand this is the same feeling she must have when I circle various sports cars in the classified ads—things I would like to have, things that I show an active interest in, but that 99% of the time I would not buy.

Pull those chin straps tight guys, the Sugar Ray Leonard of shopping is warming up and wants to spar with you. Whapada - Bapada, Whapada - Bapada, Whapada - Bapada, Whapada - Bap.

Wait until you see all of the sh-tuff that you can buy for an infant. Excuse me? A six hundred dollar dresser that is two feet high? This, mind you, is not an antique! This dresser is made out of pine, cheap pine! It is not burl, or walnut, or cherry wood; it is cheap painted pine!

Well, let's just begin with what a baby shop's salesperson, your wife, and what all of her books consider necessary and standard items: Room painted $450, with Winnie the Pooh tree, or some other children's theme (actually, of all the excess expenditures, this one is pretty cool); Italian designer crib $400; the aforementioned sheet and bumper set $420 ON SALE! (boy, she's saving us a fortune); Italian designer changing table $210 for the "my husband's a cheap bastard" model and $350 for the one that appeals to "our needs"; matching designer dresser $600 "a must for those overdressed, well primped kids we used to hate in grade school"; and last but not least, wooden louver window shades $120 if you paint and install them yourself.

The above list does not include important necessary items such as two baby car seats $200; a play pen $95, so the little bugger doesn't crawl away at the first chance it gets from the Italian Imagoofball designer room getup, and the much needed infant-seat/stroller-pram combo $135, to keep your arms from falling off from carrying your prodigy everywhere. Lest we forget, the optional swing and rollabout $100.

If we guys did not have a say (which remains to be seen), our wives would be coerced into spending $2870 today! This doesn't even include diapers, clothes, formula and blankets for the little one. And my wife is a frugal shopper. The prices listed here are the fruit of sixty hours of laborious research and shopping and are the best sale prices in ninety square miles! You could double these prices, if you didn't bargain shop and compare prices from store to store.

I will not, under any circumstances, ever be persuaded that we need to spend **TWO THOUSAND EIGHT HUNDRED & SEVENTY DOLLARS** on the things listed above. This extreme fetus materialism (the thang ain't even got eyes yet!) is a product of expert marketeers and social manipulators playing off the extreme joy, emotion, and naivete of new parents.

Before I continue (read: vent), let me assure any females that may be reading this: I consider a crib a necessity; I could be persuaded about the necessity of a fixed place (kind of like a tool bench) to change the baby's diapers, especially if I have to change them; two car seats are a must; and I applaud any interest that my wife shows regarding the improvement of our home.

Also, I must openly admit a few things: I am professional salesman. I do believe in buying the best quality that I can afford. I love antique furniture and exotic sports cars. While watching television I turn off the volume during commercials to avoid uninvited sales pitches. I throw into the outside garbage can all catalogs and unsolicited junk mail before I enter my home.

I am warning you to be prepared. Materialism has reached into the womb. Because the youngest boomers are now having babies, and our young .com society is so caught up in instant materialism and gratification, there is more sh-tuff than you could dream of being marketed to your wife and sold as necessary to the wellbeing of your impending child. And, as a salesperson, I have to applaud the effectiveness of the sales pitch. What a primal, heart-string-pulling ploy, "for the health and safety of your child." How could anybody but a cheap heartless bastard not get pulled into this?

Here's what I recommend, guys. Before the child is due, let's set up a savings account for our kids. Anytime that we feel we are being suckered into buying something not absolutely mandatory for the child's existence, let's put that dollar amount into the savings account for his or her college fund. This non-spending (read: saving) could be done throughout the first eighteen years of the child's life. Because we are actively saving at the time we are about to be suckered out of our hard earned cash, we don't have to feel *guilty* (the reverse sales pitch) for not buying an unborn child a $1,200 matching Italian designer bedroom set because we elect to purchase for our child something more important: a better future. This money can be saved and spent on a college education.

And if you question this reasoning, as my Aunt Penny did with, "What if your kid doesn't want to go to college? You can't make 'em go."

I'm sorry, I can't help you there. That is a value that you will have to instill in your child throughout its life. However, if the little bugger-head doesn't want to go to college, after you've saved all of that money for it to go, and you have this huge pile of cash sitting there... at least you have done your parental duty...

Hey, no guilt here...

We'll see you in Bora Bora in 2020.

chapter eight

She Barfed

Day 69.

She barfed. Once. It happened a week ago. She was in her car at approximately 8:00 a.m. ready to leave for work, when she had to run back inside the house and HURL!

She called me about it later that day, and she was surprised at my reaction. Even though we were talking on the phone, and she could not see what I was physically doing when she heard those raucous cheering noises, she asked me if I had my hands above my head signaling Touchdown. I was busted! I told her that yes, I was proud of her hurling efforts, and that we needed to celebrate, embrace and share the joy of each aspect and nuance of this pregnancy.

She thinks I'm nuts.

Otherwise my wife has had no ill effects from this pregnancy except for some rather finicky eating habits. The other night I spent hours shopping and preparing our favorite Hunan sauce, fresh vegetables and chicken for a stir-fry feast. She walked in from work, saw the piles of readied veggies and turned a beautiful shade of velamint green. I ate Hunan alone. . . Now when she asks me what I want for dinner, I always respond the same way, "I don't know, what do you want?" This strategy seems to be working.

chapter eight.2

Showing Off

Day 77.

The other day my lovely wife, speaking to no one in particular, said aloud, "Look!"

When I did not immediately respond, she repeated in a louder tone of voice, "LOOK!"

I turned to see her lying on the couch with one hand holding up her shirt and the other pulling down her stretch pants, exposing for the first time, her lower stomach bulge to me. I am sure this was done, in part, to garner admiration and, in part, out of sheer awe. It was one of the neatest things so far... A definite pooching, melon-shaped mound protruded from her lower abdomen. She, I could tell, was proud of herself, so I went over and bent to admire it. It was smooth, and firm to the touch, similar to a budding un-ripe watermelon, but not so taut.

I can't wait for this thing to grow.

chapter eight.4

Melon Heads

Day 91.

Have you ever had a cast on a broken arm or leg? Have you ever had the desire to buy a new car? Did you notice that during these events your awareness of like items in your surroundings expanded, and you saw more casts on other people, and more like vehicles because of this?

Have you noticed that since you found out you are pregnant, you see more pregnant people, and notice babies and children like never before?

Well, be prepared for the attack of the melon heads. You will see them everywhere. Perhaps they were always there, and you did not notice them before, but you will now. Everywhere you look you will see the cutest little babies with heads of various shapes. In an effort not to seem so emotional, so attracted to these little creatures, I came up with an evolving slang terminology: melon heads. I include gourds and large tree fruit into the mix as we see fit.

You see, my dad is a produce man. And being born in Oklahoma, and raised in California, I have been exposed to great amounts of different kinds of produce, and almost every kind of melon that is grown. And just as melons are different shapes, baby's heads are different shapes... I kinda pieced together this "melon head" terminology in order to communicate my admiration and astonishment to my wife without seeming overly sensitive and involved. It is now not unusual for me to come home and say to my wife, "You should have seen the casaba head I saw today! The size of that kid's head was enormous." And then trailing into one of the funniest scenes from *So I Married an Ax Murderer (1993)*, in my best Scottish accent, "Head. Head. Look at the size of that naggin, it should have its own solar system!"

This phenomenon happened again yesterday when I saw the cutest little pumpkin head in the ski lodge at Alpine Meadows, being toted around by its gourd-headed mother. I have to admit that I was drawn to it. I had a feeling that I've never felt before. I wanted to snatch that kid out of its mother's arms and play with it.

The feeling I had yesterday reminded me of an event I now recognize as my first conscious awareness of wanting to be a father. Ten years ago, while having my car serviced I saw a six-year-old girl asleep in a new Acura Legend. She was slumped forward against the shoulder belt with her huge honeydew head almost hanging into her lap. I remember watching for a few seconds amazed at the limberness of her little neck, thinking how sore I would be if I had fallen asleep in that position. She had a willow-like neck and her head seemed so large, so disproportionate to her little neck and body. I was smitten. Willow necks with melon heads.

The reason that I am writing this (it reads kind of mushy and lame as I re-read it) is that as guys we do have paternal feelings, we just aren't programmed to speak of them openly and freely. We come up with funky little humorous ways to (not) describe our feelings, when we have them.

Some friends came to visit us during our pregnancy. They brought their one-and-a-half year old daughter Samantha. She is so charming, and so beautiful. She is much like both of them, yet different.

Early one morning, Samantha did a header down an entire flight of stairs and thumped her melon hard on the bottom handrail post. **OUCH!** She screamed at first, cried for a little while afterward, but then seemed fine. I, however, am still affected by it. Hell, the fall alone would have put me in traction. I was informed later that this is a natural learning curve, and all children learn and re-learn about the dangers of stairs by doing a header down them at some point in their lives. After witnessing the fall, a farmer-like protectionist feeling welled up from within.

We must protect our melons. We must band together and protect our children - not only from falling down the stairs but also from cars, mean old stray dogs, evil people, the boogieman, and all of society's ills.

How are we to do this? It is all so overwhelming! Maybe I'm the melon head, but how are we to do this?

William Grant Eppler

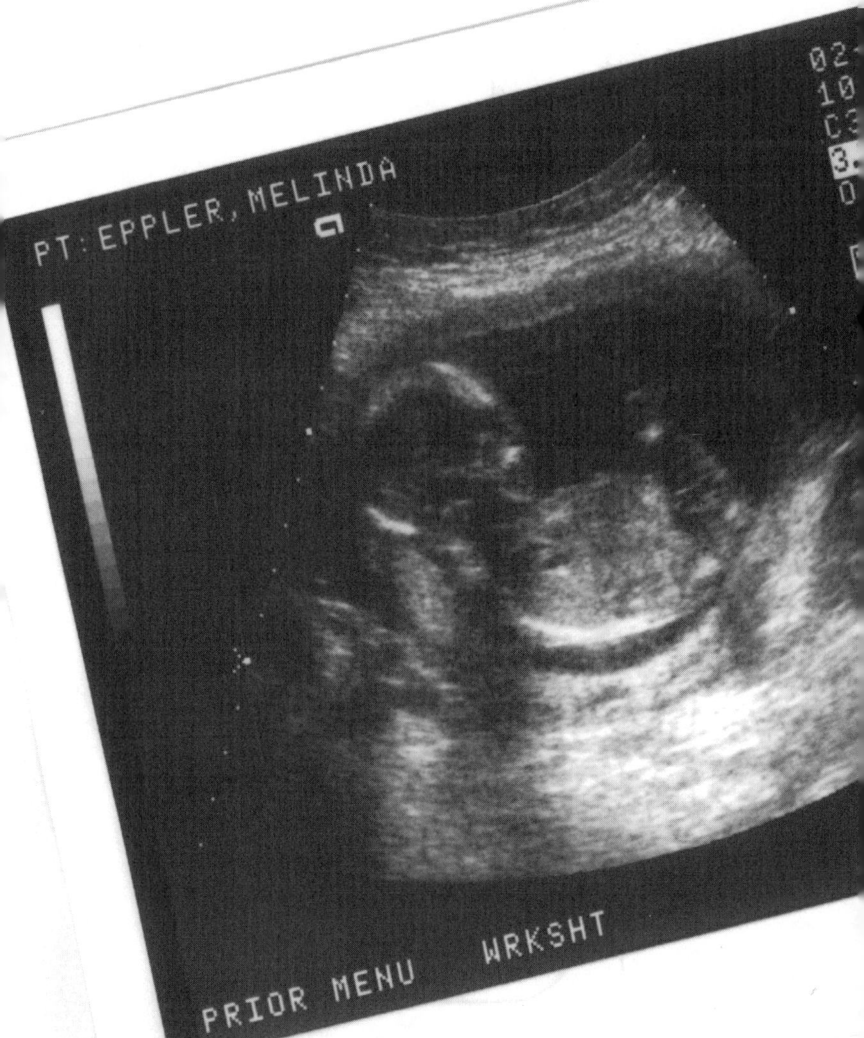
PT:EPPLER,MELINDA
PRIOR MENU
WRKSHT

chapter nine

Keeping the Appointment
Going to the Sonnet Gram with Your Wife
and Mother-In-law

(A story within itself)

Day 98.

For all of these years, you have all tried to pretend that you and your wife aren't having sex, that you didn't have sex when you were dating and have never even thought of having sex in cars, boats, and planes; that you certainly do not do the "mystery dance" whenever possible (when she reluctantly relents). And *wham*... there you are standing in a dark cubicle with the arch rival of your sex life, looking down at your pregnant wife (her pregnant daughter), partially exposed, viewing the tumbling life inside of her, trying to act normal, and being somewhat congratulated (not overtly of course!) for your mystery dance prowess. Believe me, it has been four days since we all were there to witness the sonnet gram, and I am still thinking about it.

The sonnet gram is, in and of itself, definitely new-age, meaning it completely weirded out my mother-in-law (and my mother when she saw the video tape of it). Technology is on the cusp of going way too far. You can actually see the little bugger swimming around in there. The clearness of the view, and the sterile neutrality from which the technicians approach their job, lends to the overall feeling that you are an intra-generational, cosmic peeping tom, and that the *Blade Runner* police are coming after you.

To lighten the mood I made a few "fetal" attempts at humor, but to no avail. It was generally uncomfortable for all of us. The technician (someone that you have never met heretofore) herds you, your wife, and your mother-in-law into a small cubicle. There your wife lies down on a small table, bares her lower midriff and gets her stomach slimed by the technician.

Then the tech turns a bunch of knobs, dials and doodads, and grabs something that looks like a cross between a computer mouse and the laser-reader that the checker at Home Depot uses to find out that whatever it is you waited fifteen minutes in line to purchase does not have a price on it. The tech then does some Bruce Lee Kung Fu arm exercises and then thrusts this mouse-like object onto the lower abdomen of your wife.

Because you are distracted by the overall weirdness of your mother-in-law's presence, your reactions are slow and you are just reaching out to parry the thrust from this deranged technician and save your wife when the tech announces to the world in a loud nasal whine that your wife's bladder is empty.

System overload. I'm sorry, that is more information than I needed (the entire world) to know.

"I guess we will try and continue," the tech says in a nasal whine which you pray your child will never develop.

This is the appropriate time to hand over the new videocassette that you brought. Be sure to purchase and take a new video cassette to the appointment so that you can get a taping of the actual sonnet gram to completely mystify and bore everyone that you know.

If you choose not to be informed of the child's gender you must speak up now. It is the sonnet gram that can inform you of the child's gender. Many of the people who try *not* to learn the child's gender are leaked this information by some uninformed technician or nurse.

We actively chose not to be informed of the child's gender (much to the chagrin of my mother-in-law) as we view this knowledge as one of life's last *good* surprises.

If you think about it, there are very few positive surprises left in this world because of the advancement of technology. To rob yourself of this last unknown, this last true surprise, is like unwrapping and peeking at your Christmas presents when you were a kid; you were glad to know what you were getting but bummed about what you were not getting, and further saddened on the anticlimactic day of opening. I twice said, very clearly (diligently striving not to imitate the tech's nasal whine), that we absolutely did not want to know the gender of our child. A nod is all that we received in response as the tech turned back to her precious evil machine.

"*Blink*," the screen comes on and this fuzzy, murky gray world comes to light. "Any thing that is bright white is bone, any thing that is almost white is cartilage, any thing that is gray is flesh," the tech says. This is the only thing she has said so far that doesn't make you want to reach out and throttle her.

I can only try to convey the images that this procedure conjures up. You get to see skull and hand bones, femurs, and tiny patellas, baby feets and kidneys, and if you are lucky a profile and a frontal facial picture. You can see it move in real time, swimming around, playing the inter-uterine version of "hide and go seek behind the placenta," and you can see it moving its mouth, perhaps mouthing the words to "ovaries hill ovaries dale."

I don't recommend watching this video late at night or showing this video to young children or old people. Mostly, it looks like a cross between an alien, Keith Richards, Skeletor, and James Carville. And that is enough to give even Wes Craven nightmares.

chapter ten

Itsy Bitsy Spider
(Veloce)

Day 129.

I believe it started with our aforementioned friends, the Watsons, the parents of the beautiful little girl who did a header down the stairs. Maybe it was when they arrived. As is the custom, the men filed out into the clear dark mountain evening to bring in the luggage of the latest arrivals.

We stood in the long driveway, each in silent awe, looking at the Watsonmobile. Their little Saturn's windows bulged with the contents crammed inside of it. It was grossly overloaded and hunkered down, sagging from the sheer weight of it all, complete with an extremely full roof rack sticking up into the clear dark sky. Had the auto not been new and shiny, and had I not known the occupants, the *Beverly Hillbillies* would have instantly come to mind.

"Look at all this sh-tuff," I thought to myself. "Geez Robert," is all that I said aloud. He flashed his famous grin, teeth gleaming in the darkness, always up to speed with his computer-like brain and abstract sense of humor. I think he also was appalled at the load he had brought.

"I'm never going to haul this much junk around when I have kids," I said to myself as we carried into the cabin the load the Watsons brought. However, the thought of hauling around all of this stuff stayed with me. Not being in the know, I asked my wife as we drove home from that wonderful weekend (I won at bones), "Honey, is it normal to take that much baby stuff everywhere you go?" I am sure that she could sense the "I'm going to be a father male sea of uncertainty." "Well, no, not really. They probably weren't sure about the facilities at the cabin and packed all of that stuff just in case," she replied. I could tell that she was letting me down or bringing me up to speed gently.

It was a quiet drive home and my thoughts drifted… "I own an Alfa Spider, so there is no way that I *can* carry that much stuff around. It will be just me and the kid driving around with the top down, wind in our hair, sun glasses on (you know those cool little kid sunglasses). And oh yeah, sun block. I'd better lather up the little booger head. I wonder if the car seat will fit in my little car? I am sure that it will. I wonder if I can have a little seat belt legally and safely installed on that little deck space behind the seats. Ah, that's the gas tank, probably not a good idea. Man, I don't think the stroller is going to fit in the trunk or behind the seats; I am going to carry 'the melon' around if we take my car. Wow. We can't *all three* take my car. Oh well, we have her tank we can all drive around in."

These thoughts flowed and ebbed with the tide of the "I am going to be a father male sea of uncertainty." I didn't think about this dilemma again until it surfaced two months later. I was on a back-nine tee box with my Saturday golfing buddy, Doug. Doug, who has seen me unloading my golf clubs and bag, separately, from different compartments of the Alfa on many occasions (hey, it is the only way they will all fit inside!) asked succinctly, "What are you going to do with the Alfa when the baby comes? You can't drive it around in that little car. What if something were to happen?"

I was doomed. What if some drunken idiot were to run a red light and T-Bone us at an intersection? The seed of auto doubt had sprouted eight weeks ago and here was Doug fertilizing it.

I said casually, "I'm not worried about it. Melinda said that it was no big deal, she didn't seem concerned," as I stepped up to the ball and shanked it into the trees. But, from that other fairway forward, I did worry about it. My budding paternal feelings manifested themselves in the future auto-healthcare issues of my child.

It was springtime, the best time of year to sell a convertible, and I put our beautiful Alfa in the paper to sell it. Not to brag; it was "One of the cleanest, best cared for, most attractive 40,000 mile Alfas ever. Sapphire metallic blue, tan Ricarro-type leather seats, perfect condition, flawless synchros, engine and transmission." I put the ad in the paper, and received twenty-two calls the first weekend. The first person who came to look at it said he'd buy it, no questions asked, no negotiations. I had asked a fair price, and he was a fair guy.

He was coming to pick up the car, and my youth, the next day.

I hoped that he would take good care of them both.

William Grant Eppler

Chuck Chuck

Bo Buck

Banana Fana

Fo _uck

Fee Fi

Mo Muck

Chhhuuccckkk!

William Grant Eppler

chapter eleven

Naming Names

Day 132.

"Marial," she said. "I like it," I replied. "Isabella Garcia?" she asked. No doubt after Jerry Garcia, one of her life-long idols. "Nix, you can't name her after Jerry Garcia! I thought we said no musicians, otherwise we are naming whatever it is Stevie Ray Vaughn!" "Never," she replied. "Hendrix? Bradley?" I offered. "For a girl? What are you, nuts?" she asked.

Interestingly, we were able to pick out a boy-child's name rather easily. It is the girl-child's name we are having problems with. We play this never-ending game of "Nix" and "What are you, nuts?" I find the process of coming up with a name to be fun, that is until there are more than two people involved in the discussion.

Never-ever-ever-ever-ever-ever-ever-ever-ever-ever mention that you are having trouble choosing a name, especially around family members who have been imbibing. What will inevitably happen is that you, because you can, will make an all-out attempt to immediately anaesthetize yourself with adult beverages. After the third, fourth and fifth time the same person says, "What about Rose? I like the name Rose," you will be sorry the topic was ever broached, and you will be up at 3:45 a.m. looking for an Alka Seltzer.

Hey, Seltzer is kind of a neat name! Which reminds me of a David Lettermen show that I saw. The guest was Demi Moore. Ms. Moore was pregnant with her second child and was evidently having trouble selecting a name. True to Late Night form, Demi brought her own list that she and her husband Bruce Willis had made. The list was entitled, "Top ten names that we might name our child:"

10) Beavus
9) Forklift
8) Kemo Sabe
7) Ibuprofen
6) Siskel
5) Dr. Pepper
4) Marmaduke
3) Manute
2) Retsyn
1) Buttafuoco

Erudis, Lotrimin, and Acetaminophen could be added to this list to help round out the cool semi-medical terms.

It must be noted here that guys and gals approach the child-naming problem-solving concept from two different viewpoints. Gals generally think of wonderful poetic "got a ring to 'em" type names while guys try to diminish the future possibility of their child being made fun of, getting the crap kicked out of them, or even worse than that, not getting the babes in high school. I agreed on the proposed boy's name of William Berkeley or "Berk" because William is the family name (from my side of the family, of course), "Berk" is a strong, tough name, and "Berk" is a guy who gets all the chicks.

So, if you and your wife have as much trouble agreeing on a name as my wife and I did, it is probably due to the different approaches the two of you are coming from and the different criteria you each are using to measure a proposed name. It is believed that people live up to, or down to their given names. Perhaps this is one of the reasons people change their names. A name can make or break a personality, so it is a huge responsibility to name a human being.

Along these lines, nicknames are of importance too. Have you ever heard of a CEO of a major corporation or of an elected President of the United States whose nickname was Critter?

NOTE: Names can be found in the most awkward places and at the most awkward times. I found the best name for a girl while gardening. I was trimming the flower garden and cutting the ivy back when it came to me...

Ivy Eppler.

My wife immediately said, "Nix." Now that I've planted the seed, hopefully, Ivy will grow on her. I know she has shades of doubt about the name, but she said she would "leaf" it until the child is born. I am still rooting for Ivy.

William Grant Eppler

William Grant Eppler

chapter twelve

In Yo Dreams Motorhead!

Day 145.

8:32 am. My heart skipped a beat as the words filtered into my mind. "I signed you up for LeManz classes," she had said. I could not believe it! After all the years of reading auto magazines and drooling; after retooling four or five really bitchin' Alfa Romeos; after mentioning ten or two thousand times that I had always wanted to be a race car driver; after mentioning five or fifty thousand times that I wanted to take a professional driving class at Sears Point or Laguna Seca; after showing her article after article, advertisement after advertisement for these types of racing schools, my loving wife endeavored to fulfill one of my primal wishes: she had signed me up for LeManz classes! "At the Skip Barber Racing School?" I asked incredulously. My heart was missing every other beat like an old overheated Volkswagen Rabbit in need of a new rotor and distributor cap. I knew then that this woman was my truest love on earth.

"What?" she asked, with a confused look on her face. "No," her face now squinched, "at the local hospital."

Like a hot air balloon crashing to earth, the realization came to me. "Lamaze Classes," I said barely audible, feeling like a kid who has just been diagnosed with the mumps during summer vacation and banished from the rest of the family and all of his neighborhood friends. "Gr-r-r-eat, when do they start?" I asked trying to sound alive... er... I mean enthused. "They start a month from Monday and are held every Monday night from seven to nine-thirty. There are seven classes," she said as if she were imparting the keenest tidbit of information. "Well, at least this time of year they won't interfere with Monday Night Football," was the only redeeming thought I could come up with.

chapter thirteen

Who, Me?

Day 161.

If you haven't yet noticed…no one is noticing you.

You could show up at the next social function with a purple goatee, nose, nipple and tongue rings (and if you have these already you could show up without them, freshly shaven and in a three-piece suit) and no one would notice you. The content of any and all questions asked in your general vicinity will now be about her and the child.

You will notice that your wife's friends and family are excited for her. They show a daunting amount of concern for her mental and physical well-being. They write her letters, they take her to lunch, and throw her parties. **She has a social support system.**

Even your own family will speak to you with giddiness about her, yet without uttering a single syllable of concern for _your_ physical and mental well-being. Your own friends (all three of them) who may have spent two hours in the last two years with your wife will bypass you in their questions and ask, "How is she doing? How is the baby?"

Because you are a male, it is assumed that there will be no change within you, and therefore there is no reason to ask about your state of being. It is assumed that there is no extra stress in this for you. I found myself asking, "Why is it that we guys do not ask how our expectant father friends are doing, and lend an ear for a while? Why is it that we don't celebrate this momentous occasion together?

Why is it that we don't take our expectant father friends fishing, or golfing, or to lunch? Why do we not throw each other baby tool and toy parties?" It would be a blast! Can you imagine finding real miniature golf clubs, and fishing rods? In the immortal words of Thomas Magnum, "I know what you are thinking," this guy doesn't have any friends, and up until now, I would have told you that I had some of the most awesome, stud-ly, uncles, family, and friends around.

Sadly, what I think has happened is that we men have allowed society to diminish a father's role in a child's life, and therefore we place little stock in one another's roles as fathers. It's too damned bad that we've allowed our parental position to be diminished to the point where a guy doesn't celebrate the single most amazing thing in his life, FATHERHOOD, with his friends.

So, when you hear of a pal who is expecting, take some time out of your hectic life to lend an ear, a hammer, or a day fishing or golfing. If you've got the social skills, put together a small guy's party and do something fun, anything to celebrate his expectant fatherhood. If you don't want to have a party, take the guy out, rip the top off a cold one, and let the poor guy vent.

chapter fourteen

The leManz Phenom

Day 224.

Oh, my. Rod Serling where are you? We have just entered a time and space that bends the constraints of reality, the "Pregnancy Zone!" Man, oh man, are you guys in for it! I'll tell you what, the only other place you will find so many nervous guys is… in the waiting room at Vasectomies R Us. I found myself longing for my seventh-grade catcher's mitt 'cause there were plenty of women who looked ready to drop. I have never seen so many pregnant women in one room!

The LeManz experience is far and away one of the weirdest experiences that a guy can live through. There you are with fifteen other dudes and their humongous wives, and by custom you guys are not allowed to talk to each other. When introductions are made, the women folk will introduce themselves and you, in some surreal pregnancy credo, sharing more information than you wanted or needed to know. "Hi, I'm Stacie, this is my husband George, we are due September 2nd. This is our first child. I'm feeling some discomfort, not sleeping real well. I have occasional "show" and I have to pee every hour! We think it's going to be a boy." George will sit there (looking as if he got caught doing something antisocial) and not say a word. Introductions will go around the room with the female introducing the male, who sheepishly grins and looks down at his hands as if he were three weeks old and had never seen them before.

Interestingly enough, this is the one place that women kind of let their hair down. They dress in funky comfortable stretch-type clothing. They sit with their legs spread apart, and believe it or not, they belch occasionally and even let one rip every now and then, blushing various shades of red. I would swear I was in the guys' locker room at the gym the way the women felt free to cut one loose. Of course my wife blamed every errant fart on me (what am I now, a practicing ventriloquist farter?).

As I looked around the room, all of the other guys were also catching their wives' elbows in the ribs, except for the lucky guy whose wife it was that ripped it. He feels confident that he now has one stocked in the fart karma bank.

Enough about that, let me now inform you of some mandatory pieces of information to make your LeManz classes as informative as possible.

Word Definitions

Show:
Leakage from your wife's underside. A misnomer because she won't show it to anybody but you, and nobody else wants to see it.

Cervix:
Not a Mexican beer, it is the opening where the "drain plug" is holding the water and child inside.

Dilation:
The measurement of the opening of the cervix from which your child passes from your wife's body into the world.

Nickel:

Five cents, the size of your wife's cervix at two centimeters.

Vanilla Wafer or Oreo:

The size of your wife's cervix at three to four centimeters.

Centimeter:

One of those hairy caterpillars.

A European measurement, which brings back into focus the reason for the existence of the metric system, and obviously points out that European males are better lovers 'cause they evidently got there first and staked a claim.

Rice cake:

The size of your wife's cervix when she is in "real labor."

Philly cheese-steak sandwich:

Something that is "brought up" in a video you may have to endure. Never feed your wife one of these after thirty-six weeks!

Bags of waters:

Another interesting term used in the video mentioned above. The east-coast woman who coined this term was referring to her amniotic fluid, which surrounds your child and protects it from the wipeout your wife will inevitably take (while walking) at some point during the pregnancy.

The Kegel Elves:

No comment.

Frank:
A position that your baby can assume prior to birth. Honest!

Jim:
The guy your wife went out with for three years (and almost married) before she met you.

Brutally Honest!

The 5 Stages of labor (as per the leManz instructor)

Pre-labor:
The LeManz instructor actually suggested that the women go the mall to shop to take their minds off of the pre-labor pain. I wonder where this woman thinks my wife has been for the last six months?

Early labor:
When to go to the hospital. Pains coming (to your wife) five minutes apart consistently. It is suggested that you stop at the drive-up epidural station in the parking lot.

Active labor:
Possible irritation, possible cursing, your wife may say mean things to you. For the first time the LeManz instructor has said something that I can see happening.

Transition labor:
1/2 to 1-1/2 hours of contractions with only one-minute rests between them.

Pushing:

What the nurses and doctors will do to you if you are in their way.

Actual drawings (recreations)
made by the leManz instructor:

chapter fourteen.5

Disney's Anesthesia and Nipple Classes

Day 228.

The exact moment that I became interested in the anesthesia and nipple classes (offered for a nominal fee by our local women's hospital) was the same moment that our female LeManz instructor likened the birthing of a child to the passing of a large grapefruit from a guy's southern region. As she said this while looking directly at me, we immediately signed up for the anesthesia class and then went out to dinner where I anesthetized myself from the sobering thought of her descriptive analogy.

Word Definitions

Ocean Spray:
The new term for flatulence in our household thanks to the above analogy perpetrated by the LeManz instructor.

Lactation Consultant:
The dream job of every fourteen-year-old boy.
$40 to $65 per hour with low overhead and huge fringe benefits.

Nipple:
Just a device for the kid to get nutrients.

lunch truck:
Formerly called breasts, these pairs of feeding apparatus are a part of the package deal.

latching on:
The Hoover-strength power suction achieved when an infant actually gets the nipple into his or her mouth (as opposed to his or her eye, ear, nose, etc.)

The anesthesiology class was not a barn burning, raucous party like the LeManz classes were. It was far more constrained and sterile. The lecture was given by a humorless doctor, whose only redeeming quality was that he passed around some old salad spoons circa 1938. For some inane reason he then compared them to this little plastic plunger-like suction cup. He also wowed the crowd with a minuscule fiber-optic tube and explained that this is what is inserted into a woman's outer spinal fluid sac. It carries the much-desired numbing juice that any sane guy would gladly pay for if he indeed were in the process of passing an extremely large grapefruit through his southern region.

I will never eat another grapefruit as long as I live.

Nipple classes in the other hand (boo hiss, I couldn't resist), were very informational. Did you know there are people who actually get paid for assisting with the passing of milk from breast to infant; they're called Lactation Consultants. Man oh man, where was I? Did I miss this booth during the high school job fair?

chapter fifteen

Addendum to Chapter 7

Day 234.

Do not sit in the Dutalier chair!

"What is a Dutalier chair?" you ask. A Dutalier chair is a glider-type chair as opposed to a rocking-type chair. It is a French Canadian company that makes these chairs and markets them to women, of course. The only advice that I can give you is to avoid these chairs because if you sit in one, you will end up buying one. It is one of the most cool-mechanically-inclined-comfortable chairs I've ever seen, and I have a chair fetish. If you are coerced into sitting in a Dutalier chair and then end up buying one, the best advice that I can give you is to order it from the factory through your local dealer. Be sure to ask them for the different wood color and fabric samples. From these wood and fabric samples many combinations can be designed.

Your wife may be persuaded to buy a chair in stock in a god-awful fabric and wood combination, trying to match the chair to the goofy theme of the kid's room. But at the prices quoted, this is a serious piece of furniture and I think that it should match the living room. I figure that nobody, including the baby, will want to sit in the baby's room in that chair in the middle of the night. So I suggested to my wife that we order the chair to match our living room. Then she could sit, swing (not rock), and look out the living room window in the middle of the night when she was up feeding the kid.

It was actually a great idea, and I almost received some credit for it. We were able to match the fabric to our other furniture so perfectly that you can not tell this 'mother's chair' from the rest of our living room furniture.

If matching the chair to your decor is not important, I did see copies of this chair at Cosco-type warehouse stores in some god-awful wood and fabric combinations.

Enough about the chair.

My wife advises all you fathers-to-be to be sure and get a diaper genie! And no, contrary to my first thought, Barbara Eden, from *I Dream of Jeannie*, does not pop out of the unit when rubbed and change the baby's diaper. It is supposedly a handy way to dispose of the soilings from your prodigy. Personally, I am not sure I can cram a fully-loaded diaper through the small opening without making more of a mess.

Again, watch your wallets! Priority spending only, and make sure your wife's priorities and your priorities are at least similar in nature, if not quantity. I must say, however, we have the second coolest baby room I have ever seen (I've only seen two). Thanks to the diligence of my wife, my mother-in-law, our families, and all of our friends we are now happily prepared and waiting.

P.S. So, I was a scared pansy-assed wallet-clenching mullet head. Even though I am still fending off exorbitant charges on my wife's credit card (I would hate to see what she'd have spent without my input), and even though I tried to stem the tide of expenditures, we ended up with just about every thing in the world ever conceived of for an infant!

We are now the proud owners of every item (except the $600 dresser) that I chronicled previously in chapter seven. And even though I am still amazed and have never seen such a pre-programmed, time-released expenditure in my entire life (at least the wedding had an ending in sight), it wasn't so bad because of the contributions from our friends and families. Our families gave us a crib and clothing. Friends gave us toys and clothes. Acquaintances passed on to us boxes of clothing and toys. And women with whom my wife works, some of whom I have never met, loaned us a highchair, rocker, and playpen.

Almost like a neighbor lending a hand fixing a downed fence, or someone stopping to help a stranger with a flat tire, our friends, families and acquaintances helped us in this time of expecting need. Heck, it felt as if all of humanity rallied around us with support.

It kinda makes me wonder... what if all of us lent a helping hand and acted so kind all of the time?

Pass the beer nuts.

chapter sixteen

The list

I made a Guys list of things I wanted to accomplish prior to the birth of my child. This is in addition to the list of chores that seem to form automatically from within (chapter three) or seem to magically appear in my wife's handwriting on the refrigerator. My internal list consisted of fun stuff like going on a camping trip, a big night out with the guys, shooting under eighty on the golf course, making a hole-in-one, and going on a weekend fishing trip. All of these interests will serve you well if you can accomplish them prior to the birth of your child. To facilitate accomplishing my personal pre-father goals we purchased a pager for me to wear so that I could roam Northern California unfettered until the last second.

Day 235.

I accomplished one of my lifetime and pre-father goals. I shot a by-the-book-legal-count-every-stroke **79** on a difficult local golf course. As breaking eighty has been a lifelong dream and pre-father goal of mine, afterward I thought to myself, "Now we can have the kid." I also came soooooo close, within six inches, to holing a 174 yard five iron on a par three. And yes, I made the putt for birdie!

I am still working on the hole-in-one, the fishing trip, and the big night out with the guys (my best friend in the whole world stood me up! I don't think he realizes that I am going to be busy for the next eighteen years!), but for some reason I am now ready to have a kid.

If you had told me at the beginning of this endeavor that there would come a time when I would think I was ready to become a father, and I would be somewhat secure in my thoughts about *being* a father, I would have told you that you were crazy.

I now know why it takes nine months for the gestation of a human embryo. Actually two reasons spring to mind:

1)   It takes nine months to get all of the stuff prepared and ready for the melon head.

2)   It takes nine months of hard work to get an errant golf game under control and shoot a 79!

I think that by my accomplishing the chores list of Chapter Three as early as possible, it allowed for the personal growth (and diminished NCGA handicap-index) I needed to be ready for this event. I am now ready and we are waiting.

.MCA RECORDS

Side 1

STEREO

GEMA/
BIEM

TOM PETTY AND THE HEARTBREAKERS
PACK UP THE PLANTATION - LIVE

1. So You Want To Be A Rock And Roll Star 3:30
   (J.McGuinn-C.Hillman)
2. Needles And Pins 2:23 (J.Nitzsche-S.Bono)
3. The Waiting 5:08 (T.Petty)
4. Breakdown 7:43 (T.Petty)
Produced by Tom Petty and Mike Campbell.
℗ 1985 MCA Records,Inc.

252 704-1

LC 1056

33

William Grant Eppler

chapter seventeen

The Waiting

Day 241.

4:20 a.m. 80% thinned out but zero dilation; bummer. Our due date is just days away, my wife is so huge her own friends have likened her critical mass to that of a bovine. I have never seen a woman carry a baby so low and far forward as my lovely wife.

Our doctor recommended another sonnet gram. Again, I told the technician that in no way did I want to know the gender of the child. I asked her to tell me when she was "filming" the child's lower regions so that I could avert my gaze. 8lbs-8ozs she estimates (+ or -10%). Very little amniotic fluid. My wife is a quart low and there's nothing I can do about it. The doctor has basically said, "tough nuggies-not yet" in response to my wife's repeated requests to induce labor.

My wife is not thrilled.

We need her cervix to open-open-open.

One thing was discussed at our last appointment that hasn't been clinically mentioned since our first pregnancy test: **SEX! YES!** Believe it or not, sex is good for baby, good for the cervix, and good for the process. Amazingly, it was actually brought up that sex could help move things along. It was not a doctor's order per se and the doctor did not write out a prescription for one act every four hours or anything like that. However, sex was mentioned in passing as something that can help and damn it, I wanted you to know about it. I don't know why this subject is so taboo with doctors and LeManz instructors. If we were trying to get pregnant they would surely assist in figuring out her fertile times. I mean, it's not like we all haven't... you know... that's kinda why we're here.

Anyway, we're waiting. The room is ready. Both cars are washed, waxed, and full of gas. The lawn is mowed. The trees are pruned. The wood is stacked for winter. All light bulbs have been replaced. The house is actually entirely clean. Come on over! Our people-to-call list, complete with phone numbers, is typed and packed. Our bags are packed and sitting by the front door. The camera is ready although we still need to buy film. Dang, I need film! I need cigars! I need a flask of whisky! Where is my best man? Oh, different social function. Guys should have a mid-husband to help them through this ordeal.

Of all of the work to prepare for this event, of all of the mental gymnastics, the mental and physical changes, the manual labor, the perceived and realized financial hardship, the waiting is the hardest part. Tom Petty and the Heartbreakers were right.

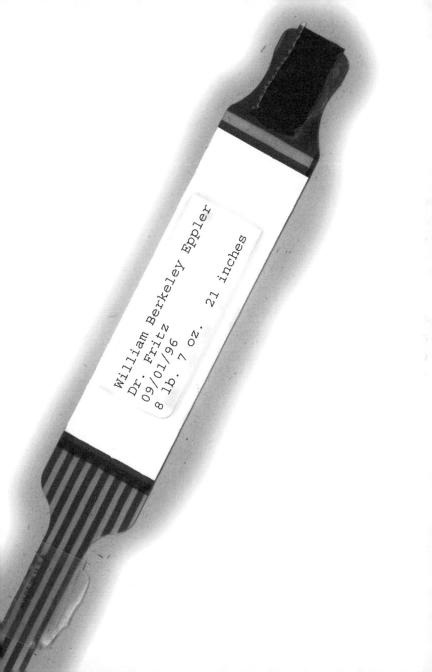

William Berkeley Eppler
Dr. Fritz
09/01/96
8 lb. 7 oz.   21 inches

William Grant Eppler

chapter eighteen

It Happened One Night

Day 245.

1:15 am. Through the misty clouds of broken sleep the words drifted down to the core of my conscious mind.

"Grant, I think my water just broke."

I sat up from the coma-like sleep with such force that I pulled a muscle in my neck and it sent shards of pain throughout my body. Head slightly tilted, I looked for where I thought the voice had come. Melinda's gentle laughter filled the air as she was only fifteen feet away and watching me. Tears of mirth which she was unable to stop, referring to my bohemian-just-awakened hairstyle, the rapidity of my ascent to consciousness, and the contorted look of pain and fear on my face. Through her continued laughter she panted, "You look just like Kamari (our Labrador retriever) when you ask her if she wants to go for a walk!" The dog, who had remained spread out and asleep on the floor throughout this ordeal now sat up rapidly and looked at Melinda, tilted its head slightly just as I was doing, perhaps thinking dog thoughts and processing her words slowly, "Did you say walk? Daaaa, its awful dark, its awful late, but I'll go for a walk. Ya, O.K., wag, wag, wag. Ya, let's walk! Are you serious? I want to walk! Wag, wag wag."

The dog and I are sitting there looking at Melinda and she is now laughing so hard she is crying, holding her sides, leaking fluid from both ends with each spasm. Kamari and I are both awaiting the next logical command "get dressed" or "go get your leash," both somewhat unsure if she is serious. Melinda could not stop laughing, but the dog was smart enough to lie down and go back to sleep. I however, entered a new phase of manhood; the infamous lawbreaking-gravity-defying "get your leaking-laughing wife to the hospital" phase.

Amazingly, and perhaps due to the fact that it was 1:15 a.m. and we'd only been asleep for about two hours (I know, we are old fogies), I could not think of what to do first. Should I shower, eat, get dressed, go to the bathroom, call an ambulance — better yet; the life-flight helicopter, pop the champagne, or help her practice our LeManz breathing techniques? Aarghh! Nobody had told me about this… this was not covered in the classes. Dad sure didn't bother to let on about this!

So, I took a quick shower, fumbled around and got dressed. I was having a hard time deciding what to wear as I didn't want to look like the family moron. We had each packed a small bag as we'd been directed to do. I loaded the car while my lovely leaking wife got dressed and did her make-up. While she was very calm, I was in a wild-eyed panic. When I went into her bathroom to tell her I was ready, I noted that she was wearing a beautiful dress and looked lovely. She eyed me in the mirror, turned around, laughed, and said, "You are not going to wear that, are you?" I was wearing pressed slacks, matching socks, dress shoes, matching belt, a button down shirt and a sweater vest, just perfect for a semi-casual day at the office and a perfect match for what she was wearing! I responded, "What's wrong with this? You are all dressed up. I want to be properly attired when my child comes into the world!" She laughed and said, "I am going to take this off as soon as we get to the hospital, you are going to have to wear that for a day or so. You ought to put on some comfortable clothes, like sweats." To which I countered with, "Yea, well, you are all dressed up, I was just following suit." I went and changed into jeans and loafers but I kept the button down shirt and sweater vest.

We actually stopped at an all night "Stop and Rob" and bought our supplies while she was in early labor! Upon exiting the parking lot and heading for the freeway, the urgency of the situation overtook me. Well, honestly, I was overtaken by a Highway Patrol cruiser that had pulled alongside me. Looking down at the speedometer I noted that I was driving 70 miles per hour, which didn't bother me until I realized seconds later that we were not on the freeway yet! Unfazed, the Highway Patrolman waited for me to cower to his omnipotent Mustang. I gladly slowed to 40 mph and made some hand gestures in the dark that I hoped he would interpret and translate to, "Oh my god, My wife is leaking! I am scared shitless and trying to get her to the hospital. We're having a baby!" I was never good a charades, but after we slowed down, he glowered at us, sped off, and we continued unmolested. Moments later my wife asked me to slow down, as I was again driving too fast.

Something peculiar happened at the hospital when we pulled up at the maternity emergency entrance. I've already chronicled in detail how we were dressed and that the car was freshly washed and waxed. A security guard was asking other fathers to go park in the lot after dropping off their wives. I pulled in and he motioned me to the curb. After I assisted her from the auto, the guard motioned to an attendant with a wheel chair who rushed over, passing two other pregnant couples in pajamas, to assist my lovely wife. The guard then told me to escort my wife inside. He also told that if I left my car there he'd keep an eye it. The only reason that I can figure the security guard and attendant were so helpful is that we were nicely dressed and everyone else looked as if they had just awakened and had driven to the hospital in their jammies.

The lessons I learned

Drive safely and sanely.

If you can dress nicely for the first hour or two, it pays off. As Melinda had already filled out all of the hospital forms in advance, and requested a single room (an extra $35 per day well spent!), we did not have to wait in line to be assigned a maternity room. We were treated as if we had entered a fine hotel, while other couples, unfortunately, were not.

Don't forget towels. Have four throw-away towels in the car. One to stem the tide of leaking fluid, one folded in half on her car seat, one on the floor to absorb any fluid that leaks by, and one to mop the beads of sweat from your brow.

Be sure to have film, two big liters of water, Gatorade, three cans of Pringles, some caffeinated sodas (JOLT anyone?), candy bars, and any other food source that you can think of help stave off hunger pangs. You may end up at the hospital late, after everything is closed and it could be hours before there will be anything open to help quench your wife's thirst and hunger needs.

Also, bring a roll of quarters or some dollars in low denominations for the vending machines.

Be extremely polite to the nursing staff when you first arrive, and again when they change shifts.

Be sure to bring a change of clothes (sweats?) and a comfortable pair of shoes. The idiot author of this book forgot to pack his tennis shoes and wore his sweats, hospital scrubs and penny loafers around the maternity ward looking like uncle Fester. Plan on standing on your feet for eighteen hours, with little sleep, while leaning over the bed to assist your wife. If the birth takes less time, you will be fortunate!

Bring a pre-made sign that reads "Please close the door" to help remind the hospital staff.

Be sure to ask the hospital staff any and all questions you can think of. If you feel that a staff member isn't answering your questions or is acting inappropriately, ask for another staff member to replace him/her. (Unfortunately, we had an anesthesiologist who was an absolute asshole; if I ever see him out on the town he will need the services of a dentist and a proctologist!).

Hey Batter-Batter-Batter-Batter Hey Batter-Batter-Batter-Batter Push!

Depending on the disposition of your wife, things can get a little dicey. She may not complain to the nurses, doctors, and family gathered in your room. But she may inform you of her displeasure. This can help to relieve her stress and it is your job; Take it. Do not, however, feel obliged to pass it along to your family and friends. They will not take it so well coming from you.

I hope your delivery is fast and easy. Ours was not. About ten hours after arriving, and well after the LeManz techniques were wearing thin on all of us, the doctors determined that our child was stuck. Its head was too big and was now lodged catty-wampus in the birth canal. Don't you think we could've figured this out before the ten hours of pushing?

Feeling like it just wasn't going right I quietly asked the nurse, out of Melinda's earshot, if we were going to need a C-section. She nodded affirmative. Not to worry, she said, the vital signs were strong and we were in no danger. So of all things, and without telling Melinda the news, they upped Melinda's painkillers and told her to take a nap and get some rest! And she did! Through the contractions and all, my lovely wife rolled on one side, closed her eyes and began to snore softly.

After coming all this way, after doing all of the aforementioned work, after attending all of the doctors appointments, after all of the shopping excursions, after watching all of those movie matinees to help avoid the summer heat, after writing seventeen chapters of this book, after waiting on needles and pins for the last week, after having only six hours of sleep in the last 48 hours (I'd been up partying with my neighbor the night before), after only literally minutes of sleep in 24 hours, after being awakened and rushing to the hospital in the middle of the night, after drinking five cups of coffee, three cans of Pepsi, and two liters of water, after TEN FRIGGING HOURS OF LABOR AND LEMANZ BREATHING TECHNIQUES, there I was standing in the maternity ward, dazed, buzzed, and alone.

I wasn't totally alone, I mean our folks, and her brothers were out in the waiting room (my sister decided to go to a soccer game instead).

So, I did what any guy in my situation would do, I asked the nurse to come and get me when Melinda awoke so that I could be there for support when they told her of the impending surgery. Then I went into the waiting room and joined our families in snarfing down the pizza and beer that my father-in-law (what a stud!) had sneaked into the waiting room.

Melinda slept soundly for an hour. Unfortunately, even I though I had clearly instructed the nurse to summon me when Melinda woke up, I was not there when the nurse informed her that she was going to have a C-Section. I am still pissed about that.

Off to Surgery
Breathe... Damn it, Grant... Breathe

Whatever has happened until now seems to fade far into the distance.

Time bends and blurs; people come in and out, family comes and goes, nurses and doctors guess this and that. When the doctor and the room and the medical staff is ready, man you had better be ready too.

My wife was awake and feeling no pain. She was attended to by a nurse and an anesthesiologist, while I was immediately led down a series of hallways and curtly instructed to put on my sterile scrubs, and wait sitting in a particular chair in a hallway. I felt we were being rushed now that they were ready, but that very little if any thought was given as to whether we were ready. So, I asked all of the questions I could think of. And when the doctor seemed impatient, which made me begin to feel like my questions and concerns were unimportant (chapter 13), I began to ask more questions of the doctor, "Why only on this chair? Wait here for how long? Where's my wife? How are we doing? What is this procedure like? What can we expect? Is there a danger either to my wife or to the child? What should I look out for? Can I assist in some way? Do I get to watch? Will I still get to cut the umbilical cord and catch and hold my child after it is born?" I asked, and then waited for answers. After a pause, I added, "Hell, I wouldn't let you work on the transmission in my car without first asking a few questions. What's the deal?" The doctor finally realized that I had obviously not been briefed on what was about to happen, and she began to answer my questions. "We don't want you to touch anything because we are about to go into a 'sterile' environment. We are asking you to wait until the room is prepped and Melinda is brought down. She's on her way down now and will be in the room and prepped when an attendant comes for you in a few minutes. Both the child and Melinda are fine, we don't expect any complications. Since your child is stuck in the birth canal, and we tried like heck for a vaginal delivery, a C-section is the best answer now. You will be able to watch from only one vantage point. After the child is born, you can cut a section of the cord. You will be allowed to hold the child after we clear its airways, etc... But Melinda will not be allowed to hold the child alone because of the anesthesia. I need to go get ready now."

Somewhat placated, I sat on my one chair and waited for the attendant to come for me. It was a long, lonely, and tense five minutes. When he did come for me, I followed him into a room where my wife, lay arms extended from her sides, forming a T shape. I was instructed to stand on one spot and not move. My wife was draped in green surgery covers with her midriff exposed and its size and shape truly looked surreal: A wonderfully beautiful woman with this huge alien-like bulge exposed and illuminated by the surgical lighting. The doctors proceeded to apply what appeared to be a big round piece of scotch tape (it was made by 3M!) to my wife's belly and draw on it with a felt pen. They then cauterized as they sliced her open, to keep bleeding to a minimum. There was very little blood. After the initial incision, they used ladles to spread the opening they had just created. As I watched, the doctor put both of her hands and entire forearms inside the opening and pulled. Nothing happened. The doctor repositioned herself to get more leverage, took a firm grasp, and pulled again.

In a split second, she was holding my child upside-down by the ankles and barking orders to the staff. The child didn't make a sound but I could swear the kid was looking, albeit upside-down, directly at me! I immediately moved off my spot to walk around and hold my child but was also barked at and ordered to go to a little table in the corner of the room. "It's a healthy boy," the doctor exclaimed. "Look at how red and healthy he is," exclaimed one of the nurses, "and he's not even crying… Oh my, Dad, he's looking at you." As it was the first time I had been referred to as "Dad", it took me some time to figure out that the nurse was speaking to me. I squeezed my wife's hand and asked her permission to leave my post and go hold our son. She nodded and said, "I want to see him."

When he was delivered to the little table, I saw for the first time what appeared to be a major deformity; his face and head were uneven and squinched to the left and he had a massive black and blue cone-shaped head. Tears streamed down my face, and I felt the worst gut-wrenching fear I have ever felt. "Don't worry Dad," the nurse said after seeing the expression on my face, "They all look like that after they've been stuck in the birth canal for awhile. The head will reshape in about thirty minutes." I cut the umbilical cord, held my son to my chest, and carefully took him to see his mother who wasn't yet allowed to hold him because of the anesthesia.

William Berkeley Eppler
was quietly born at 2:42 PM on Day 245.
He is a healthy and happy baby, and he has rarely cried since.

The only constant that I can share with you about childbirth is that when your child comes, you will experience the most amazing rush and feelings of pride, sheer joy, and true love for your wife and newborn child.

It is the best feeling on earth. Let us cherish it for the rest of our lives.

About the Author

William Grant Eppler is first and foremost a husband to his wife and father to his child. He graduated Summa Cum Laude with a Bachelor of Arts Degree from California State University, Sacramento just nine months following the events chronicled herein.

He is currently re-learning how to play and writing his second book entitled:

Every **Guy's** Guide
— 2 —
Babies and Kids

The following is a chapter from the new book.

William Grant Eppler

Epplerlogue

Every Guy's Guide
2
Babies and Kids

Chapter Three
Hero for a Knight

"Every father should be a hero to his children," Dr. Ernie Olson had said. "Not a superflying caped crusader, but a hero to his children. A man to be there for them when they need you." Perhaps what Dr. Olson said was lost on some of the youth in the audience but his words rang true with me. I've thought about this concept many times since I heard him say it.

After some research, I concluded that studies and polls indicate most men plan on being better fathers than their fathers were to them. As is true with this guy, I plan on being a better father than my father was; he is a good father but as society has changed and men are now allowed more access to their children, there is room for improvement.

The following is my first experience of being a hero for my child. The intrinsic satisfaction I felt during the moments described below can never be fully shared or conveyed through words. I didn't fly through the air or leap tall buildings with a single bound, I was simply a soothing, caring father for one moment in time.

My son Berkeley probably doesn't remember this event, but it is a moment that I will never forget. And an event I plan on repeating, in various ways, throughout his life.

Hero for a Knight

Almost two months old.

It was a rough night. The muffled cries of an unhappy person cut like a well-honed scalpel through the various levels of my comatomatic sleep and throughout the night, everywhere. I arose to find my lovely wife half-asleep, sitting on the couch, holding the surgeon of sound, both looking confused and frustrated.

"I'll take him, honey," I said as I pawed at the encrusted mucus that had enveloped my right eye. "It is my turn."

"No, it's ok. I've got him... He's been like this for over an hour. He's really upset," she replied half-heartedly, half asleep, but still able to impart an intended meaning of, "You can't handle this!"

"I can handle it! I'm his father. You go to sleep," I said clad in full-father regalia; robe askew and half-open, stretched-out T-shirt, boxer shorts, and customary black dress socks with house slippers.

She took note of the authoritative tone in my voice, my prestigious apparel, the awfully late yet extremely early hour, and the general shuffling demeanor with which I stood. "Good luck Dad!" she said as she handed me the Physician of Phonics. "Nice outfit," she added with a grin as she padded down the hall to bury herself in the dark warm comfort of goose-down.

My new shoulder mate scrunched up his face, turned, and erupted with shocking veracity directly into my left auricle, "Whaaaaaaaaaaaaaaaaaa!"

"It's ok now, Berkeley. Papa's here, it's ok," I said in a comforting and soothing tone of voice, gently but firmly patting his back in an upward motion, trying to finesse a burp from the little man. At this precise millisecond, the value of impending hero-dom was the farthest thought from my mind.

"Let's go for a little walk-er," I said. Upon hearing my own words said aloud, I knew that these were the wrong words to string together into a phrase in our home. Upon hearing these same words, my 95 pound golden retriever shot up from a sound sleep and raced for the front door sending the throw rugs, hall runners, and their subsequent pads skidding across the hardwood floor. "Back," I commanded to the dog. She hedged and gave me just enough room to open the front door and then shot out through the open door as I stepped onto our front porch.

"Whaaaaaaaaaaaa!" another plaintive wail sounded from my left shoulder and echoed throughout the neighborhood.

"Berk, Berk, Berk, Berkeley. Berk, Berk, Berk, Berkeley," I sang to him. He looked at me, pursed his lips, made a pouty-I'm-still-mad expression and stopped crying. Figuring I had just righted some major transgression, I forged into a few verses of the second song of the now famous Eppler medley "If you're a mullet, and I'm a mullet, and your mom's a mullet too, if I'm a mullet, you're a mullet, what are we gonna do?" With him now almost smiling, I cleared my throat, lowered my voice, and launched into the third song of the medley; one of the best songs ever written and performed (Bing did it best! on Swing'n with Bing! 1989 re-release). "I've flown around the world on a plane, I've danced Flamingos Pasadobles in Spain, you know, the North Pole I've charted—but I can't get started with you. What to do? Baby I'm so blue. On a golf course I'm under par—on a nice day, Metro Goldwyn has asked me to star—we haven't talked pay, I've got a house that's a showplace, still I can't get no place with you..."

Smiling now he quietly coo-ed along with me. "You're so

supreme, lyrics I write of you and I scheme, just for the sight of you dream, still you're my waterloo. I've been consulted by Dwight D., Princess Kelly had me to tea, with Queens I've ala carted, but I can't get started with you."

And there I found myself, walking the sidewalk in front of our home at 3:15 a.m., dressed as I was, with my eight-week-old-son ensconced in the crook of my left arm. He was now cooing softly and grinning from ear to ear, yet I had a feeling that there were more smiles out there in the darkness. I spied a shadow moving inside my darkened home and I knew that Melinda, the ever-vigilant mother, had been watching us and was smiling also. I grinned with the realization that the Eppler family was being smiled down upon by whatever forces there are in the universe, we were as one, and truly blessed. That is when I remembered the words of Dr. Olson and smiled with the knowledge that I had won one for all fathers and had been a hero for one moment in my child's life.

The point here is that even though we might have had a rough go of it last year, we are now fathers! We have an obligation, and ample resources to fulfill this obligation. Whatever time and energy constraints we previously held, whatever barriers we had set for ourselves, can and will be obliterated.

We are now fathers.

At the school where I attended the fifth grade there is a brass plaque embedded in the courtyard wall that reads, "No man stands so straight as he who stoops to help a child."

"NO MAN STANDS SO STRAIGHT AS HE WHO STOOPS TO HELP A CHILD"

IN MEMORY OF

NORMAN R. SIEFKIN

PRINCIPAL 1959 - 1969